QUICK STaRT™ draw, PAINT, STICK

SAFARI ANIMALS

carolyn Scrace

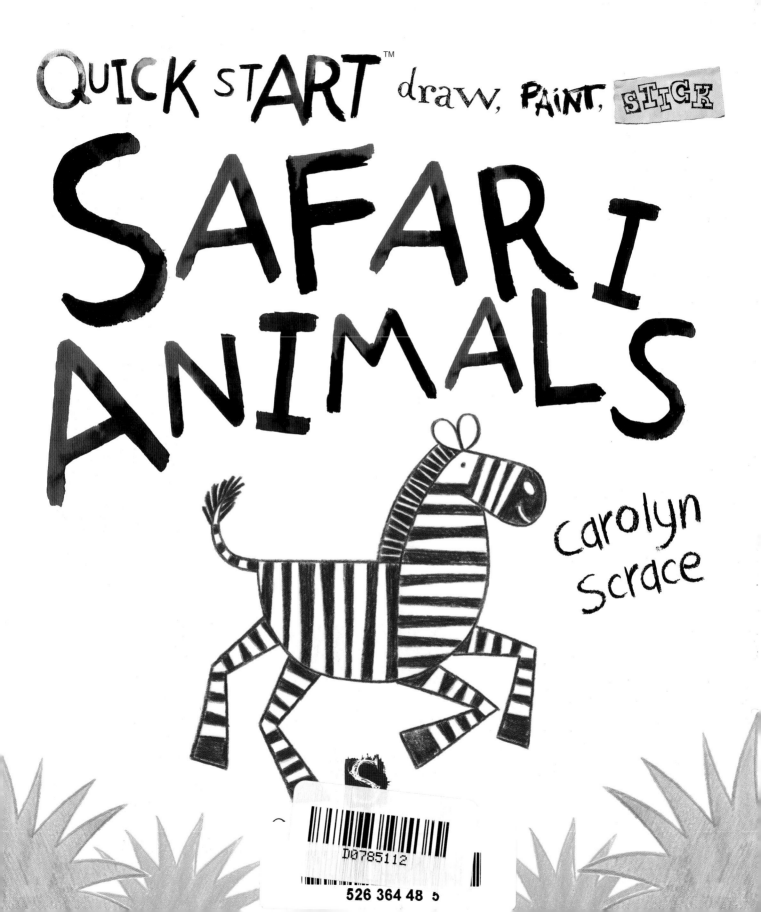

Artist

Carolyn Scrace graduated from Brighton College of Art, England, after studying design and illustration. She has since worked in animation, advertising and children's publishing. She has a special interest in natural history and has written many books on the subject, including *Lion Journal* and *Gorilla Journal* in the *Animal Journal* series.

How to use this book

Follow the easy, numbered instructions. Simple step-by-step stages enable budding young artists to create their own amazing works of art.

What you will need

On each page you will find a list of basic art materials. Some crafts involve the use of scissors, so adult supervision is advised.

Published in Great Britain in MMXVIII by Scribblers, an imprint of
The Salariya Book Company Ltd
25 Marlborough Place,
Brighton BN1 1UB
www.salariya.com

SALARIYA
SCRIBO BOOK HOUSE SCRIBBLERS

© The Salariya Book Company Ltd
MMXVIII

ISBN-13: 978-1-912006-20-5

1 3 5 7 9 8 6 4 2

A CIP catalogue record for this book
is available from the British Library.

Printed and bound in Malaysia.

Visit
www.salariya.com
for our online catalogue and
free fun stuff.

Contents

Crayon Zebra

You will need:
- Paper
- Pencil crayons

Pencil crayons are ideal for drawing and colouring. Build up richness by layering colours, or create exciting textures by scribbling.

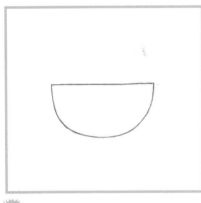

1 Use a black crayon to draw a semicircle for the zebra's body.

2 Draw in a long, rounded shape for the zebra's head.

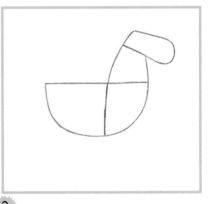

3 Draw in its neck. Extend the back line down to the zebra's belly.

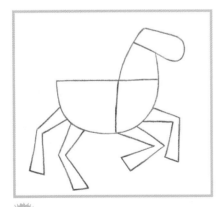

4 Draw in the zebra's two front legs, then add its two back legs.

5 Draw in its ears, mane and tail. Add lines for its muzzle and hooves.

6 Draw in the zebra's eye, nose and mouth.

Colour in the zebra's
muzzle and hooves.
Draw and colour in its
black stripes. Finally,
crayon in its mane.

Draw in the sun, sky and
hills in the background.
Add a grassy plain for
the zebra to run on.

Waxy Tiger

You will need:
- Wax crayons
- Thick cartridge paper
- Watercolour paints

This technique uses wax to resist water-based paints. Use a wax crayon to draw onto paper and paint over the top with watercolour paints – the paint will run off crayoned areas.

1 Use a black crayon to draw a long, rounded shape for the tiger's body.

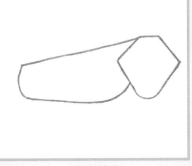

2 Draw in a simple shape for the tiger's head.

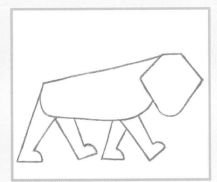

3 Draw in the tiger's front and back legs and its paws.

4 Add the tiger's tail, ears and nose. Draw in a curved line for its belly.

5 Use a black wax crayon to draw in the tiger's eyes, mouth and stripes. Add its claws.

6 Paint the tiger's face, body, legs and tail with orange watercolour. Paint his nose brown.

Use a white wax crayon to draw in the tiger's whiskers. When you paint over the background, his whiskers will stay white!

Add some leaves to make a jungle scene. Paint in the background with watercolours and leave to dry.

Tissue Paper Leopard

You will need:
- Black felt-tip pen
- Thick cartridge paper
- Coloured tissue paper (orange, yellow, black and white)
- PVA glue

Make sure you have clean hands when working with tissue paper.

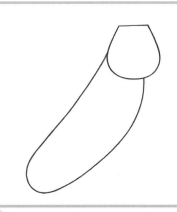

1 Use a black felt-tip pen to draw the leopard's head.

2 Draw a long sausage shape for its body.

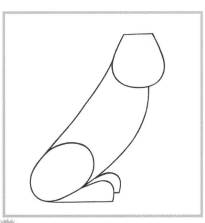

3 Draw an oval shape for its leg, then add both paws.

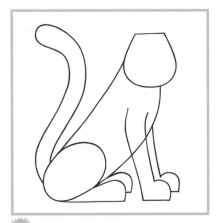

4 Draw in its two front legs and paws. Add the tail.

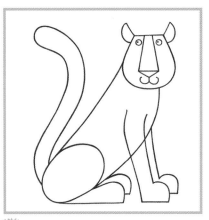

5 Draw in the leopard's ears, eyes, nose and mouth.

6 Tear yellow and orange tissue paper into small pieces to glue onto the leopard's body.

Tear out orange and black tissue paper and glue in place to make the leopard's spotted coat.

Finish off its eyes and nose with more tissue paper.

Tear strips of tissue paper to make grass in the foreground. Add more tissue paper shapes for the sun, branches and leaves.

9

Chalk Meerkat

Chalks can be used in many different ways. Try scribbling with the tip, or lay the chalk on its side to make a broad band of colour. Use your finger to smudge the chalk to create a soft effect.

You will need:
Black paper
White chalk
Coloured chalks
Scrap paper to rest
your drawing hand on

1 Use pale brown chalk to draw a circle for the meerkat's head.

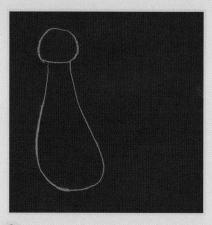

2 Draw in a long, rounded shape for its body.

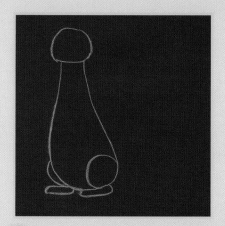

3 Draw in the meerkat's hind legs and feet.

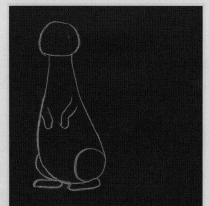

4 Draw in two short front legs.

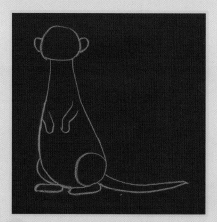

5 Add the meerkat's ears and its long thin tail.

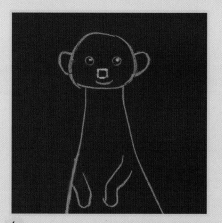

6 Use white chalk to draw its eyes, nose and mouth.

7 Add its white furry face, leaving black areas around both eyes. Then add white to its body and front legs.

Use coloured chalks to finish off the meerkat and to draw in the background.

Painted Rhinoceros

Build up the shape of a rhinoceros by painting a series of simple shapes. Draw in the detail using felt-tip pens.

You will need:

Poster paints
Paintbrush
Cartridge paper
Felt-tip pens

1 Paint the rhino's body shape: a rectangle with two rounded corners.

2 Paint a semicircle shape for the rhino's head.

3 Paint in four small rectangles for the legs.

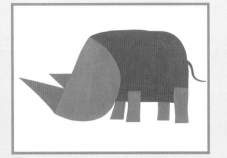

4 Paint two triangles, one larger and one smaller, for the rhino's horns. Paint in a small tail.

5 Paint two petal shapes for its ears. Paint in its eye, nostrils and three toenails on each hoof.

6 Use a black felt-tip pen to draw the rhino's mouth and to finish off its eye, horns, legs, tail and hooves.

Paint some hills in the background, then add a pale orange sky and a huge orange sun.

Paint in some trees.

Paint in a watering hole for the rhinoceros.

13

Handprint Elephant

You will need:
- Pencil
- Poster paints
- Large paintbrush
- Small paintbrush
- Coloured paper
- Felt-tip pens
- Scissors
- PVA glue

Have fun making a messy handprint, then draw and paint on it to turn it into an elephant!

1 Paint your hand with poster paint and press it down onto paper. Leave your handprint to dry.

2 Use a felt-tip pen to draw the elephant's ear, eye and tusks.

3 Add the end of the elephant's trunk and draw ridged lines on it.

4 Use a felt-tip pen to draw the elephant's toenails and its knees.

5 Draw in its tail. Paint its tusk and eye white.

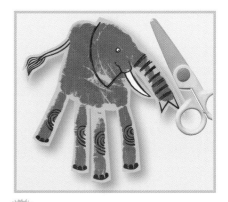

6 Cut around the elephant and glue it onto coloured paper.

Make some
fingerprint leaves
for your elephant
to eat.

Below are some more
handprint safari animals for
you to draw and paint.

Wildebeest

Giraffe

Lion

15

Paper Cup Monkey

You will need:
- Paper cups
- Poster paints
- Paintbrushes
- Pipe cleaners
- PVA glue
- Scissors
- Pencil
- Paper

These cheeky paper cup monkeys are easy to make. Why not make a whole tribe?

1 Use a pencil to draw in the monkey's face. Add its eyes, nose and mouth.

2 Draw in the area of white fur around its face and its chest shape.

3 Use poster paints to paint the monkey's face and chest. Paint the rest of the cup black.

4 Use a fine brush to paint in the monkey's eyes, nose and mouth. Add little painted lines for the fur.

5 Draw and then paint the monkey's ears and legs on paper. Leave to dry and cut them out.

6 Glue the ears to each side of the face. Glue the top part of its legs inside the cup (as shown).

Glue a pipe cleaner onto the back of the paper cup to make a tail. Bend the top round into a curl.

Here are some more paper cup monkeys to try, or you can draw and paint your own ideas!

17

Pebble Crocodile

Try to collect the flattest, smoothest pebbles you can, as these will be easiest to paint on.

1 Paint your pebble with white poster paint and leave to dry.

2 Use a pencil to draw the crocodile's eye sockets and the outline of its head.

3 Pencil in its large mouth and add lots of sharp, pointed teeth!

4 Finish drawing the crocodile's eyes. Draw in its nostrils and add ridgelines across its snout.

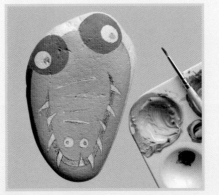

5 Use pale green poster paint for the head. Paint the eye sockets a darker green.

6 Paint the mouth red, and the edges of the pebble dark green. Add thin black painted lines to define all features (as shown).

18

Paint the ridges on the crocodile's snout dark green. Add some black lines to its eye sockets.

Paint some yellow spots on the crocodile's lower jaw.

Here are some more pebble safari animal ideas for you to paint. These pebbles make wonderful paperweights or personalised gifts.

Folded Paper Tiger

You will need:
- Square sheet of thick cartridge paper
- Pencil
- Poster paint
- Paintbrushes

Make sure you use paper that is thin enough to fold easily.

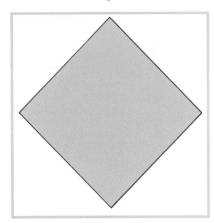

1 Paint a square sheet of paper with orange poster paint. Leave to dry.

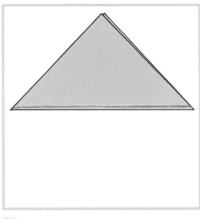

2 Place the paper painted side downwards. Fold the bottom corner up to the top corner (as shown).

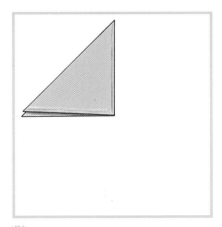

3 Fold the right corner over to the left (as shown). Unfold again.

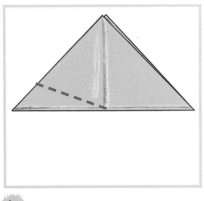

4 Fold the left corner up at an angle (as shown).

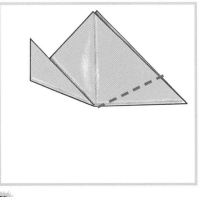

5 Fold the right corner up at the same angle.

6 Fold the top point downwards (as shown).

Now turn the tiger's head over. Draw in its nose, eyes and mouth. Add some stripes.

Paint the tiger's snout white and add brown to the area above it. Paint in the eyes and the stripes. Add all finishing details.

Try making more paper models to paint, like this leopard and cheetah!

Leopard

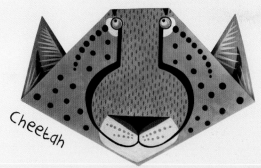

Cheetah

Printed Lion

You will need:
- Pencil
- Felt-tip pens
- Large paintbrush
- Potatoes and carrots
- Paper
- Thin sponge
- Scissors
- Poster paints

Potatoes and carrots make ideal printing blocks. Ask an adult to cut them in half or into shapes (as used here). Paint the cut surface with colour to make a printing block that is pressed down onto the paper.

1 Draw around a halved potato for the lion's body shape.

2 Now halve a small potato and draw around it for the lion's head.

3 Draw around a piece of carrot for the lion's four legs.

4 Add paint to the small potato and press down firmly to print the lion's head. Now print his mane using a small carrot stick.

5 Use the large potato half to print the body and the piece of carrot to print the legs.

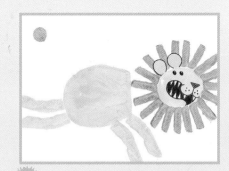

6 Use a round slice of carrot to print the lion's ears and the tip of its tail. Draw in the face with felt-tip pens.

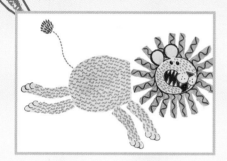

7 Use a felt-tip pen to draw in the lion's tail and its toes.

Decorate the lion's mane and fur with a variety of felt-tip pen squiggles.

Use scissors to cut the sponge into leaf shapes. Coat with paint and print the jungle background.

Have fun experimenting by printing your lion onto different coloured papers.

Folded Crocodile

You will need:
- A4 sheet of thick paper or thin card
- Poster paint
- Paintbrushes
- Pencil
- Scissors

Choose paper that is thick enough to stand up when folded, but not too thick to cut out small details.

1 Paint an A4 sheet of thick paper (or thin card) with green poster paint. Leave to dry.

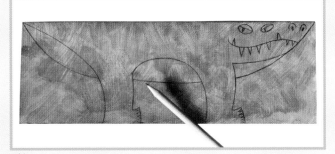

2 Fold the paper in half. Pencil in a crocodile shape. Draw in its eyes, nose, mouth and teeth.

3 Paint the crocodile's eyes, teeth, underbelly and claws with white poster paint.

4 Paint on grey stripes and orange spots. Add black outlines to its mouth, teeth, eyes and nose.

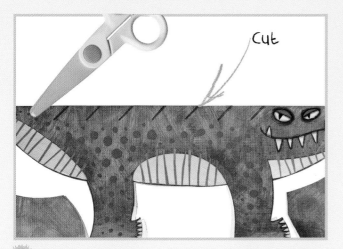

Cut

Crease Firmly

5 Pencil in a row of short, angled lines along the crocodile's back. Use scissors to cut the pencil guidelines.

6 Unfold the crocodile and lay it flat. Ease the paper cuts open, then fold each paper triangle back and crease firmly.

7 Fold the crocodile in half again and crease flat. Stand the finished crocodile up.

These paper crocs make wonderful greetings cards!

Torn Paper Giraffe

You will need:
- Pencil
- Thin paper for tracing
- Sheets of coloured papers
- PVA glue
- Black felt-tip pen

Take extra care when tearing out the paper shapes for your giraffe.

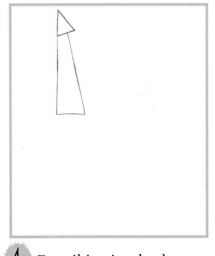

1 Pencil in simple shapes for the head and neck.

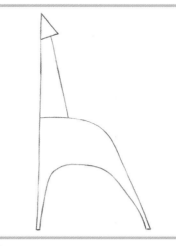

2 Draw a simple shape for the body and legs.

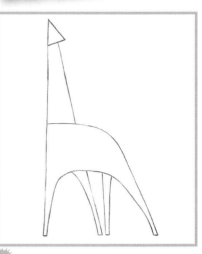

3 Add the other two legs. Scribble over the back.

4 Go over the pencil lines to transfer the drawing onto cream-coloured paper.

5 Tear all the shapes from the cream-coloured paper.

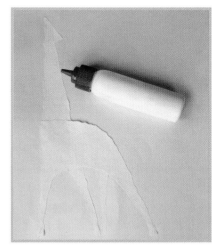

6 Arrange the shapes onto a sheet of blue paper and glue down.

26

Tear little squares of
coloured paper to make
the pattern on the giraffe's
body. Glue in place.

Tear little bits of coloured
paper to make its ear, horn,
tongue, hooves and tail.
Glue in place.

Use a felt-tip
pen to draw in
the giraffe's eye,
nostril and mouth.
Draw hairs on the
end of its tail.

Make a tree out
of torn paper with
plenty of leaves for
the giraffe to eat!

27

Collage Hippo

You will need:
- Pencil
- Paper
- Scissors
- PVA glue
- Old magazines, wrapping paper, corrugated paper, sponge, buttons, wool, foil, sequins, leaves etc.

To make a collage you need to cut shapes out of a variety of materials. Then you arrange them into a picture and glue everything in place.

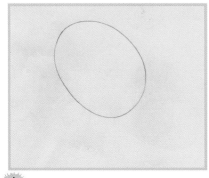

1 Pencil in a large oval shape for the hippo's body.

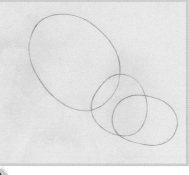

2 Draw two smaller ovals for its head and snout.

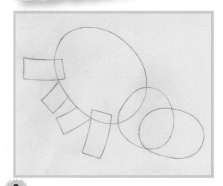

3 Pencil in four legs. Now scribble over the reverse side of your drawing.

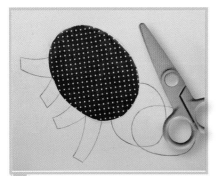

4 Lay the drawing onto wrapping paper. Go over the pencil lines to transfer the shapes. Cut out, and glue onto your drawing.

magazine cutting

sponge

5 Repeat step 4. Use magazine cuttings for the head and a piece of sponge for the snout.

6 Use corrugated paper for the legs. Cut out shapes for the eyes and nostrils. Add buttons to finish off the eyes.

Make the ducks (above) out of corrugated paper and gold wrapping paper. Glue on sequins for the eyes.

Glue on some wool to make the hippo's mouth and tail.

Make the hippo's ears out of corrugated paper and glue in place.

Add fish made out of foil and sequins, and cut up some leaves to glue on as pond weeds.

pond weed

Mosaic Snake

Make a picture or design from small pieces of coloured paper glued close together so that little of the background paper shows through.

You will need:
- Large plate
- Thick black paper
- White pencil crayon
- Coloured paper scraps
- PVA glue
- Scissors
- String

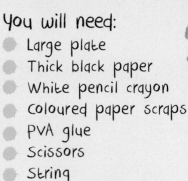

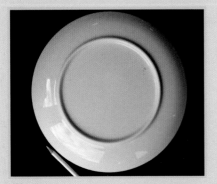

1 Place a large plate face down on a sheet of thick black paper. Draw around the plate with a white pencil.

2 Starting from the outside circle, use a white pencil crayon to draw a spiral shape (as shown).

3 Use scissors to cut around the white spiralled lines.

4 Cut scraps of coloured paper into squares and triangles. Now use PVA glue to stick the shapes onto the spiral.

5 Keep repeating the rainbow colours to finish covering the spiral snake with mosaics.

6 Draw the snake's head, eyes and nose on some black paper. Add mosaics to it.

Glue the head onto
the snake's body. Ask
an adult to make a
small hole through
the top of the head.
Tie a knot at one end
of a piece of string
and then thread it
through the head.
Now hang your
snake up above
a radiator to see
it spin.

7 Cut out the head
and fold in half. Cut out
another head-shape
and glue the folded
head on top.
Glue on a long
forked tongue
and two
fangs onto
the open
mouth!

31

 # Glossary

Collage an artwork made from various materials pasted onto a surface.

Fangs a snake's two long hollow or grooved teeth.

Mosaic an artwork made from small coloured pieces of glass or other materials.

Printing blocks hand-carved shapes used to print a design.

Technique method used to produce an artwork.

Texture the look and feel of the surface of a material or picture.

Watering hole a pool of water where animals go to drink.

Wax resist the use of a wax crayon to draw and block out areas from watercolour paint.

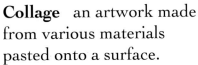 # Index